The Night Sky

by Miriam Sklar

ISBN: 978-1-338-75081-2
Illustrated by John Lund

Published by Scholastic Inc., 557 Broadway, New York, NY 10012

10 9 8 7 6 5 4 68 25 26 27/0

Printed in Jiaxing, China. First printing, January 2021.

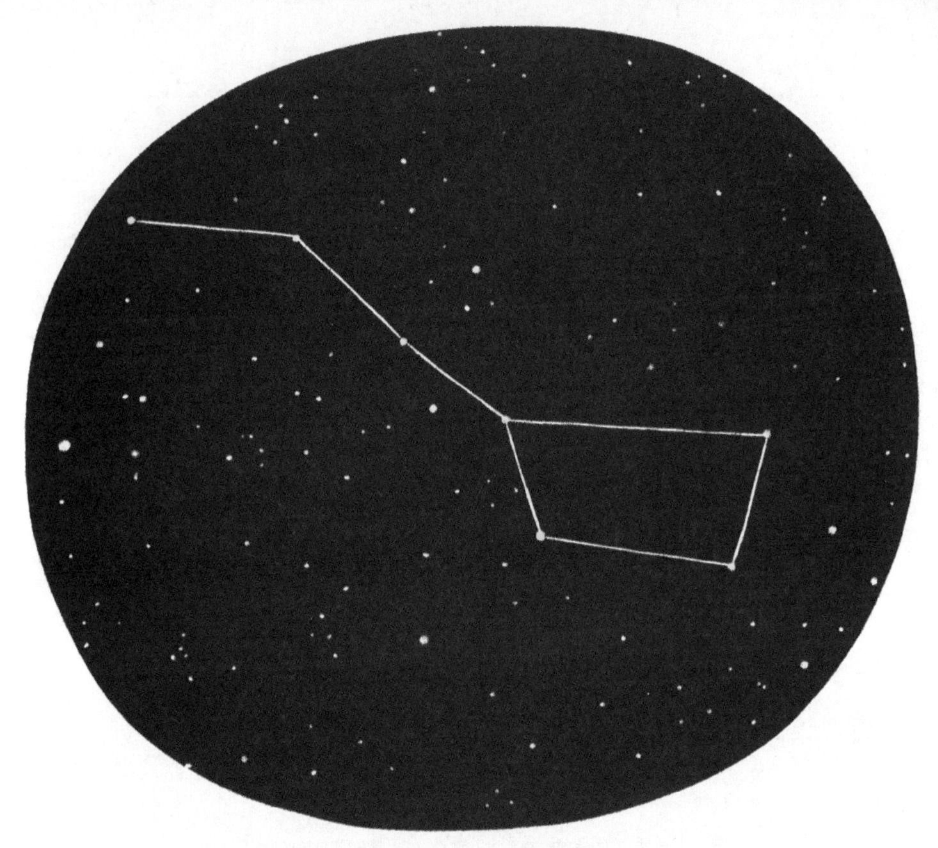

I can see a cup.

I can see a dragon.

I can see a lion.

I can see a bull.

I can see a bear.

I can see a man.

I can see a shooting star!